Weekly Reader Books
MIDDLETOWN, CONNECTICUT

Publishing, Executive, and Editorial Offices:
Weekly Reader Books
Field Publications
Middletown, CT 06457

This book is dedicated
to my mother-in-law,
Betty "Bear" Casto,
whose sense of humor has
given me sustenance over the years.

Why did the great baseball player bear
always wear a mask?

Because he stole bases.

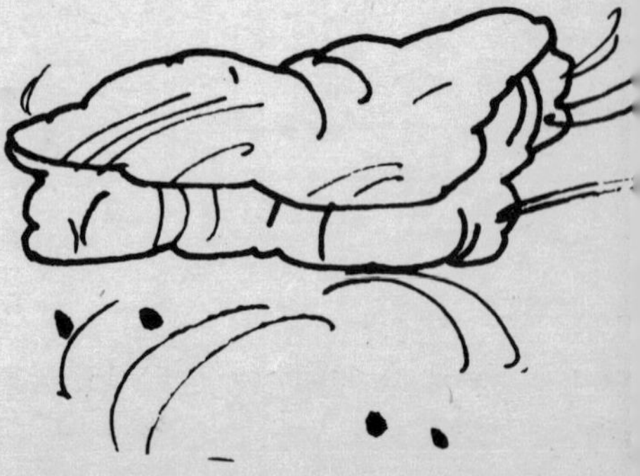

DOCTOR: My, my, you must be upset about that potato growing out of your ear.

BEAR: Yes, indeed. I sure am. I planted corn.

What happened to the bear who put dynamite into his freezer?

He really blew his cool.

What did the bear say when the judge said, "Order! Order!"?

The bear said: "I'll take a ham and tomato on rye and hold the mayo."

What do you say when you meet a two-headed bear?

Very gently, you say: "Hello. Hello."

What happened when the bear put a saddle on his stereo record?

He became a disc jockey.

Why did the bear chew up a dollar?

It was his lunch money.

Why did the bear wear boxing gloves
when he drove on the highway?

So he could fight the traffic.

Why did the bear always wear wet clothes?

Because the label said wash and wear.

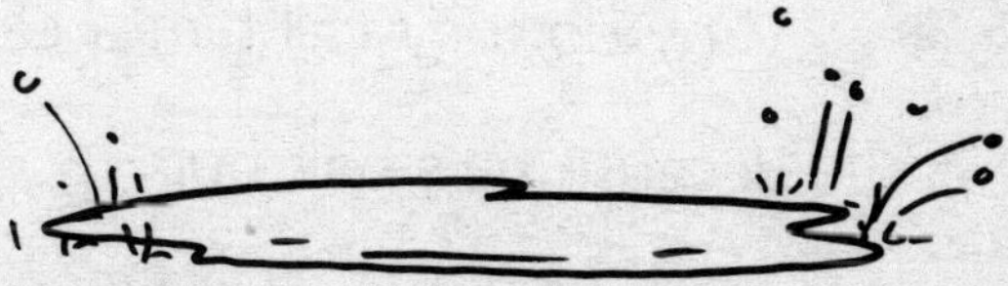

What can you do with a green bear?

Two things: (1) save him for St. Patrick's Day or (2) put him in a paper bag and he'll ripen in about three days.

Why do they call him a candy bear?

Because he's half nuts.

Why did the bear put his trumpet in the freezer?

He wanted to play cool music.

Why did the bear hide a hammer in his bed?

He planned to hit the hay.

What do you get if you cross a snowball with a bear?

Frostbite.

The bear went to the medicine cabinet and took out the medicine. Then he poured some of the liquid into a spoon and jumped up and down. Why?

The label said to shake well before using.

Why did General Bear stand behind his horse?

He figured he'd get a kick out of it.

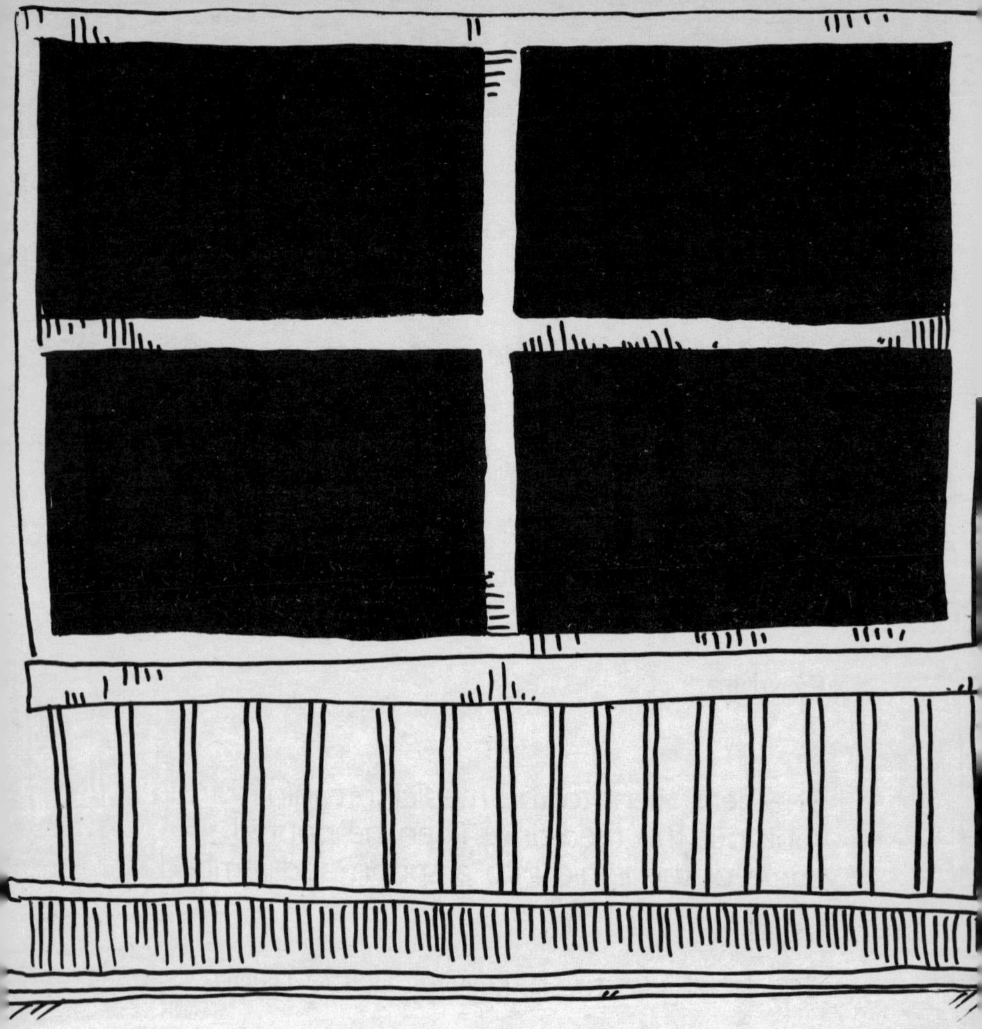

Why did the bear take a ruler to bed with him?

He wanted to see how long he slept.

TRAINER: I just trained this bear to play checkers.

KID: Wow! That must be a smart bear.

TRAINER: Not really. I can beat him two out of three games.

What's the medical report on the bear who swallowed a dollar?

No change.

What can you expect from a bear with four lips?

Nothing but double-talk.

After doing his grocery shopping, a bear went to a movie. The theater was very crowded. When the movie was half over, the bear got really thirsty, so he went out to the lobby for a drink. When he came back, he saw a fox sitting in his seat.

"Excuse me," said the bear, "I think you're sitting in my seat."

"No way, buddy," answered the fox. "Can you prove this is your seat?"

"I think so," said the bear. "I left a lemon meringue pie on it."

Why did the bear tiptoe past the medicine cabinet?

She didn't want to wake the sleeping pills.

How many bears does it take to change a light bulb?

Five—one to hold the bulb and four to turn the ladder.

A reporter for the *Bear Facts News* went into a Chinese restaurant to order sweet-and-sour chicken. He liked the dish so well that he asked for the recipe. But the waiter said, "Just like you bear reporters, we never reveal our sauce (source)."

Why did the super baseball player bear toss a ball across the table?

His coach told him to get the ball over the plate.

A bear received an electric toothbrush as a gift at his birthday party. Then he threw it in the river. Why?

Obviously, he didn't have an electric tooth.

How hot are the summers in Bear Country?

The summers are so hot in Bear Country that the bears have to feed their chickens ice or else they'll lay hard-boiled eggs.

The Fantastic Bears football team paid $100 for a new player and all they got was a quarterback.

How did the bear know she'd be good in sports?

She had athlete's foot.

Why did the bear go out of the lamp-making business?

He didn't like making so many shady deals.

Why don't bears ever tell secrets in a garden?

Because potatoes have eyes and beans talk.

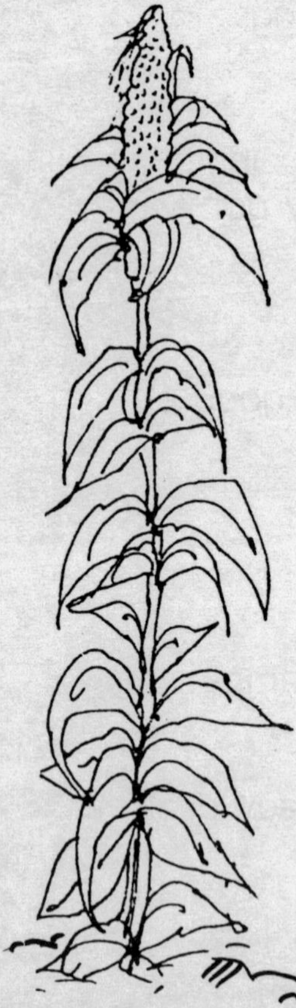

REALLY!
I DON'T BELIEVE IT!
OH YES!
NO!

A gorilla was walking down the street when he saw a bear jumping up and down on a lid over a hole. The bear kept saying "42, 42, 42, 42." The gorilla thought that looked like a lot of fun, so he walked over and asked if he could try the same thing.

The bear was in a good mood, so he stepped off the lid. When the gorilla started jumping up and down and repeated "42, 42, 42, 42," the bear pulled the lid out from under him. The gorilla fell right into the hole.

Quickly, the bear put the cover back on the hole. Then he started jumping up and down again, chanting "43, 43, 43, 43."

How can you stop a group of bears from charging?

Take away their credit cards.

Why did the bear climb up a ladder to sing?

So he could hit all the high notes.

Why did the bear put her clock into the oven just before the party?

She planned to have a hot time.

What time is it when a bear sits on your watch?

Time to get a new watch.

Late one night, a bear ran through a camp, smashing all the tents. A hunter ran out and shot the bear in his pajamas.

That's ridiculous! Bears don't wear pajamas.

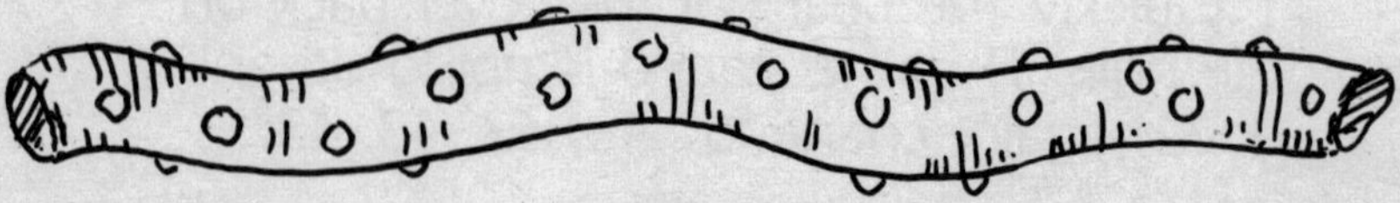

Why was the bear fired from her job in the pretzel factory?

Because she tried to straighten everything out.

Why did the bear eat the calendar?

She just loves dates.

Why did the bear throw away one of her sneakers?

She saw it sticking its tongue out at her.

FOX: I've heard that fish is supposed to be good brain food.

BEAR: We bears crave fish. I eat fish three times a day.

FOX: Well, there goes that theory!

Why did the bear start a perfume factory?

He wanted to make a lot of scents.

Why did the bear give up his watch-repair business?

He always had to work overtime.

What did the bear say when he saw a flying saucer?

No comet.

What happened when the cross-eyed bear tried to be a teacher?

He couldn't control his pupils.

Why did the bear wear a leash to school?

He thinks he's the teacher's pet.

One day a bear went wild and began eating all the watermelons in sight.

What happened?

He became a little melon-choly.

Why did the bear go to school at night?

So he could learn to read in the dark.

Why did the bear hibernate in the fireplace?

He wanted to sleep like a log.

How can you tell if there's a bear in a dark room?

You can smell the blueberries on his breath.

Why can't bears fly?

They can't afford airline tickets.

Why do bears like to ride in elevators?

It raises their spirits.

Lucy Bear went bankrupt in the laundry business.

Yeah, she's all washed up.

Why did the bear take an extra sock when he played golf?

In case he got a hole in one.

SAM BEAR: A poor bum ran into me this morning.

SHEILA BEAR: What did he say?

SAM: He said he hadn't had a bite in weeks.

SHEILA: What did you do?

SAM: I bit him.

Why did the bear become a baker?

He kneaded to make a lot of dough.

MILK
FLOU
BAKING
SODA

Why did the bear take a box of pencils to her room?

She wanted to draw the drapes.

Why did the bear become a shoemaker?

He really liked sole music.

A bear walked into a malt shop and crouched on a stool at the counter. He ordered a 50-cent Hot Honey Sundae. When the sundae arrived, the bear handed the waiter a $10 bill.

The waiter took the $10 to the cash register, then he turned around to watch the bear eating the sundae. "That bear is totally dumb," the waiter thought. "He doesn't know a thing about money."

The waiter walked back to the bear and handed him only a dollar in change.

"You know we don't get many bears in here," the waiter said. "In fact, you're about the first bear I've seen in here."

"Well," the bear growled. "At $9 a sundae, you're not likely to get many more."

Why did the bear lose his job as an elevator operator?

He couldn't learn the route.

How many bears does it take to make popcorn?

Five—one to hold the pan and four to shake the stove.

STRIKE NOW!
BEARS STRIKE
WE MUST STRIKE NOW!
STRIKE

Why did all the bears at the zoo go on strike?

They were tired of working for peanuts.

What goes *thump, thump, swish, thump, thump, thump, swish*?

A bear wearing a wet sneaker.

A man walked into a doctor's office with a bear on his head. "You need help right now," the doctor said. "I certainly do," said the bear. "Get this man out from under me."

Why did the bear sneak a saw into the poker game?

He wanted to cut the cards.

How do you know if you're in Bear Country?

By the sap buckets on the telephone poles.

How do you know when there's a bear under your bed?

Your nose touches the ceiling.

What happened to the bear who couldn't tell toothpaste from putty?

All his windows fell out.

What's the difference between a rainy day and a bear with a toothache?

One is pouring with rain, the other is roaring with pain.

What happened to the bear who fell down the well?

She kicked the bucket.

What famous bear lives at the North Pole?

Santa Claws.

Why can't bears drink Kool-Aid?

They can't figure out how to get two quarts of water into those little paper envelopes.

A bear and a fox were working in a coal mine. The fox turned on his flashlight and pointed it toward the top of the mine.

"Listen," said the fox. "I'll give you five bucks if you can climb this beam of light to the top."

"Do you think I'm stupid?" said the bear. "I'll get half way up and you'll turn it off."

BEAR: Doctor! I keep thinking I'm a pack of cards.
DOCTOR: Sit down. I'll deal with you later.

Why did the bear stand in front of the mirror with her eyes closed?

She wanted to see how she looked when she was asleep.

BETTY BEAR: I ran around the forest at midnight last night.

BEN BEAR: How come?

BETTY BEAR: I couldn't remember something and I wanted to jog my memory.

Why did the bear run around his bed?

He wanted to catch up on his sleep.

Why did the bear couple get married in a bathtub?

They wanted a double ring ceremony.

What's yellow and dangerous?

A bunch of bears hiding in a bowl of custard.

Why did the bear think the school was haunted?

She heard the other cubs talking about school spirit.

Where can a poor, sad bear always find sympathy?

In the dictionary.

Why did the bear sleep on a lamp?

Because he was a light sleeper.

What should you watch when you're talking to a hungry bear?

Your step.

One day a bear discovered a bird's nest with three little eggs in it. Quickly he sat down and began telling jokes. When he finished, he had told about 101 jokes. What effect did all those terrible jokes have on the eggs?

It really cracked them up.

JACK BEAR: I notice that Betty Bear got a job sweeping chimneys.

NANCY BEAR: Yeah. The job soots her well.

Why did the bear throw a clock out the window?

She wanted to see time fly.

SUE BEAR: Did you know that Jack Bear works as a landscaper?

LUCY BEAR: Right. He's a real down-to-earth type of bear.

Why did the bear keep a slice of bread in her comic book?

She liked crummy jokes.

Why did the bear like lightning?

It gave her a big charge.

BEAR: Doctor! Doctor! My hair is coming out! Can you give me something to keep it in?

DOCTOR: How about a paper bag?

How do bears keep cool at football games?

They stand next to the fans.

How can you help a blue bear?

Cheer him up.

Why did the bear chase his tail?

To make both ends meet.

Why did the bear stare at the ink blotter?

She found it very absorbing.

Why did Grandma Bear tie roller skates to her rocking chair?

She was tired of old-fashioned music and wanted to rock and roll.

What happened to the bear who stole a bar of soap?

He made a clean getaway.

What do you get if you cross a bear with an owl?

A huge beast that scares everyone and doesn't give a hoot.

What should you do when a bear sneezes?

Get out of the way.

What should you do if you find a bear in your bed?

Sleep somewhere else.

What's worse than seeing a bear's shining teeth in a dark room?

Seeing its tonsils.

What happened to the bear who slept with her head under a pillow?

The fairies came one night and took all her teeth away.